**Edition Schott**

Nikolai Kapustin

Николай Капустин

1937 – 2020

# Wheel of Fortune

(2003)

for Piano
für Klavier
для фортепиано

opus 113

Authorized Version

**ED 23035**
ISMN 979-0-001-20501-6

www.schott-music.com

Mainz · London · Madrid · Paris · New York · Tokyo · Beijing
© 2021 Schott Music GmbH & Co. KG, Mainz · Printed in Germany

# Wheel of Fortune

## opus 113

Nikolai Kapustin
1937–2020

**Allegro** (♩ = 132)

4